My Christmas Treasury

compiled by Gale Wiersum

illustrated by Sylvia Emrich

GOLDEN PRESS
Western Publishing Company, Inc.
Racine, Wisconsin

Fifth Printing, 1981

ACKNOWLEDGMENTS

''Christmas Morning'' from UNDER THE TREE by Elizabeth Madox Roberts. Copyright 1922 by B. W. Huebsch, Inc. Copyright renewed 1950 by Elizabeth Madox Roberts. Reprinted by permission of The Viking Press, Inc.

''The Lights on the Christmas Tree'' by Florence Page Jaques from THE CHRISTMAS BOOK. Copyright 1954 by Whitman Publishing Company. Reprinted by permission of The Nature Conservancy.

DON'T LOOK!
by Kathryn Jackson

Don't look in the closets,
Or under the beds,
Or in any mysterious nook
Where things may be hidden—
It's simply forbidden
When Christmas is coming—
Don't look!

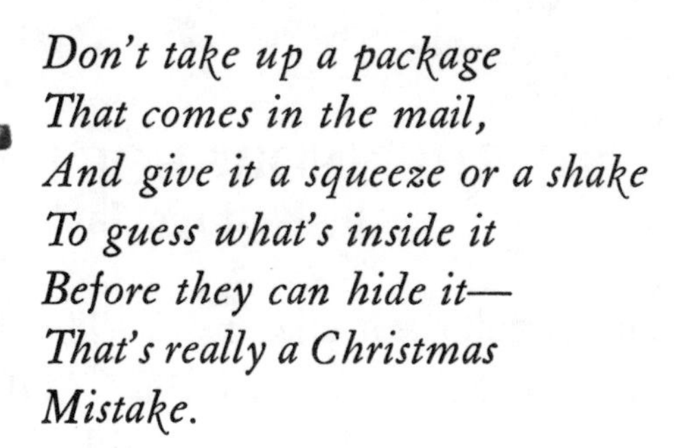

Don't take up a package
That comes in the mail,
And give it a squeeze or a shake
To guess what's inside it
Before they can hide it—
That's really a Christmas
Mistake.

Don't listen at bedtime
To hear what they're saying,
Or peep in when doors are ajar.
Hold your ears, shut your eyes,
For a Christmas surprise
Is better on Christmas,
By far!

THE SNOWSHOE RABBITS
by Kathryn Jackson

Five happy rabbits sat close to the fireplace in their snug little house. One was the mother rabbit, one was the daddy rabbit, and three were young rabbits who had never seen Christmas.

"At Grandma's there will be a bigger tree," said the mother rabbit, "lighted with candles and covered with presents for three good little rabbits!"

The little rabbits' eyes shone.

"And, of course, your grandpa will play his rabbit piano." The daddy rabbit grinned. "He'll play 'Jingle Bells,' and 'Deck the Halls,' and 'Away in a Manger.' "

The little rabbits began to hum. They knew all those songs. They knew all about Christmas at Grandma's. So they sang until their ears waggled.

Then one fat little rabbit jumped up.

"After that comes Christmas dinner," he said. "A big roast carrot basted in sugar, mashed turnips with butter, and cranberries red and shining. And for dessert, a round pudding all lighted up, with holly on top."

"I can hardly wait for tomorrow!" whispered another little rabbit. "I can hardly wait to go to Grandma's."

The mother rabbit smiled, and the daddy rabbit looked at his watch. "We'll go early in the morning," he said. "And now it's time good little rabbits were in bed."

In a whisk of a whisker, all three little rabbits were in their beds and sound asleep.

They dreamed of shining candles, and wonderful presents, and beautiful smells, and a glossy tree, and a sprinkling of snow.

But when they hopped out of bed in the morning and looked out the window, there was more than a sprinkling of snow. Snow covered the grass and all the rabbit paths. It was deeper than boots, deeper than leggings—deeper than those three worried little rabbits themselves.

"It's too deep!" whispered the fat little rabbit. "We'll never be able to get to Grandma's."

By and by the three little rabbits crept downstairs. Sorry little rabbits they were, too, full of gulps and sighs. But the mother rabbit and daddy rabbit talked happily all through breakfast, just as if nothing had happened.

After breakfast, the daddy rabbit hurried up to the attic. Back he came, smiling and proud, with some funny-looking things under his arm. They looked like tennis rackets—but who plays tennis in the deep snow? Nobody!

"They're snowshoes," explained the daddy rabbit. "They're for walking right on top of deep snow!"

The little rabbits didn't wait to hear any more. They scrambled into their warmest clothes and gathered up all their little secret packages.

Then out into the crisp, white snow went the whole rabbit family. Across the deep snow they tramped on their wonderful snowshoes.

They made big, scuffy snowshoe tracks, from their house straight toward Grandma's house, those happy little rabbits.

And as they went they sang, so Grandma and Grandpa could hear them coming:

Snowshoe rabbits in the snow,
Off to Grandma's house we go—
Holly, pudding, popcorn, toys,
Shining candles, lots of noise;
Off to Grandma's house we go!
Sing for Christmas!
Sing for snow!

WHAT CAN I GIVE HIM?
by Christina Rossetti

What can I give Him,
Poor as I am?
If I were a shepherd,
I would bring a lamb.

If I were a Wise Man,
I would do my part,
Yet what can I give Him?
Give my heart.

CHRISTMAS AROUND THE WORLD
by Gale Wiersum

Merry Christmas from around the world! We're from Spain, and we set out shoes stuffed with hay for the camels of the Three Kings. In the morning, we find gifts in place of the hay.

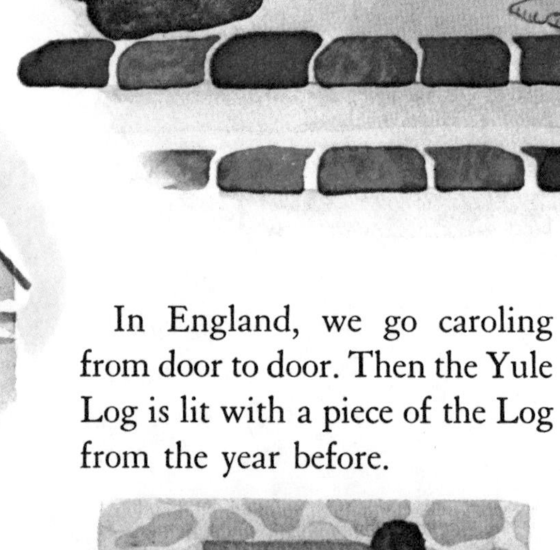

In England, we go caroling from door to door. Then the Yule Log is lit with a piece of the Log from the year before.

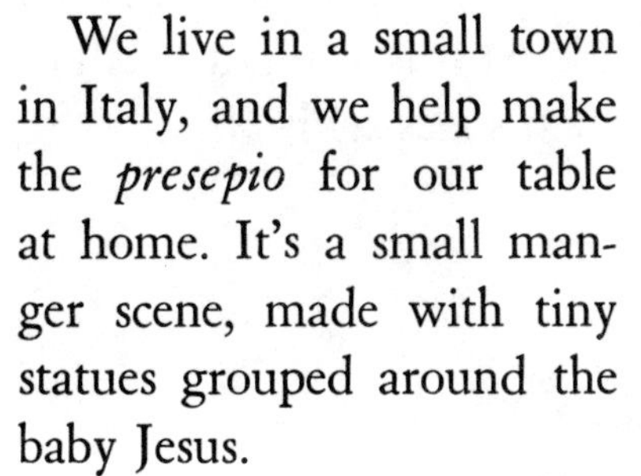

We live in a small town in Italy, and we help make the *presepio* for our table at home. It's a small manger scene, made with tiny statues grouped around the baby Jesus.

In Norway, we tie sheaves of wheat on high poles. This is our special Christmas tree for the hungry birds.

Saint Nicholas rides through the streets of the Netherlands, distributing nuts and sweets to us. He returns at night to fill our wooden shoes with gifts.

In Poland, we place straw under the tablecloth in memory of the stable. We also leave a vacant chair for the Holy Child.

Welcome to our celebration in Mexico. We're taking turns striking a hanging *piñata* with a stick. When it breaks, we'll all run for the candies that fall out.

In Yugoslavia, we try to find the silver coin hidden inside the Christmas cake. The coin brings good luck to whoever finds it.

We're from Denmark, and we believe that Jule Nissen, an elf, brings our presents. We always leave a bowl of rice pudding for him to eat. He is never seen, except by the family cat.

In the Philippines, we make colorful wreaths and chains out of tropical flowers. We wear them when we sing in the parade after church.

MERRY CHRISTMAS,
EVERYONE!

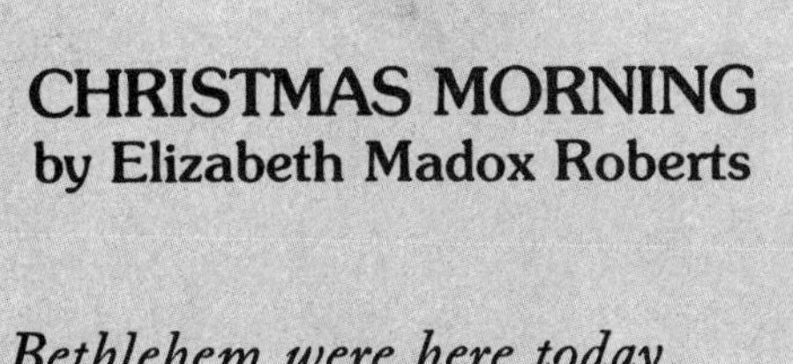

CHRISTMAS MORNING

by Elizabeth Madox Roberts

If Bethlehem were here today,
Or this were very long ago,
There wouldn't be a wintertime
Nor any cold or snow.

I'd run out through the garden gate,
And down along the pasture walk;
And off beside the cattle barns,
I'd hear a kind of gentle talk.

I'd move the heavy iron chain
And pull away the wooden pin;
I'd push the door a little bit
And tiptoe very softly in.

The pigeons and the yellow hens
And all the cows would stand away;
Their eyes would open wide to see
A lady in the manger hay,

If this were very long ago
And Bethlehem were here today.

And Mother held my hand and smiled—
I mean the lady would—and she
Would take the woolly blankets off
Her little boy so I could see.

His shut-up eyes would be asleep,
And he would look just like our John,
And he would be all crumpled, too,
And have a pinkish color on.

I'd watch his breath go in and out.
His little clothes would all be white.
I'd slip my finger in his hand
To feel how he could hold it tight.

And she would smile and say, "Take care,"
The mother, Mary, would, "Take care";
And I would kiss his little hand
And touch his hair.

While Mary put the blankets back,
The gentle talk would soon begin.
And when I'd tiptoe softly out,
I'd meet the Wise Men going in.

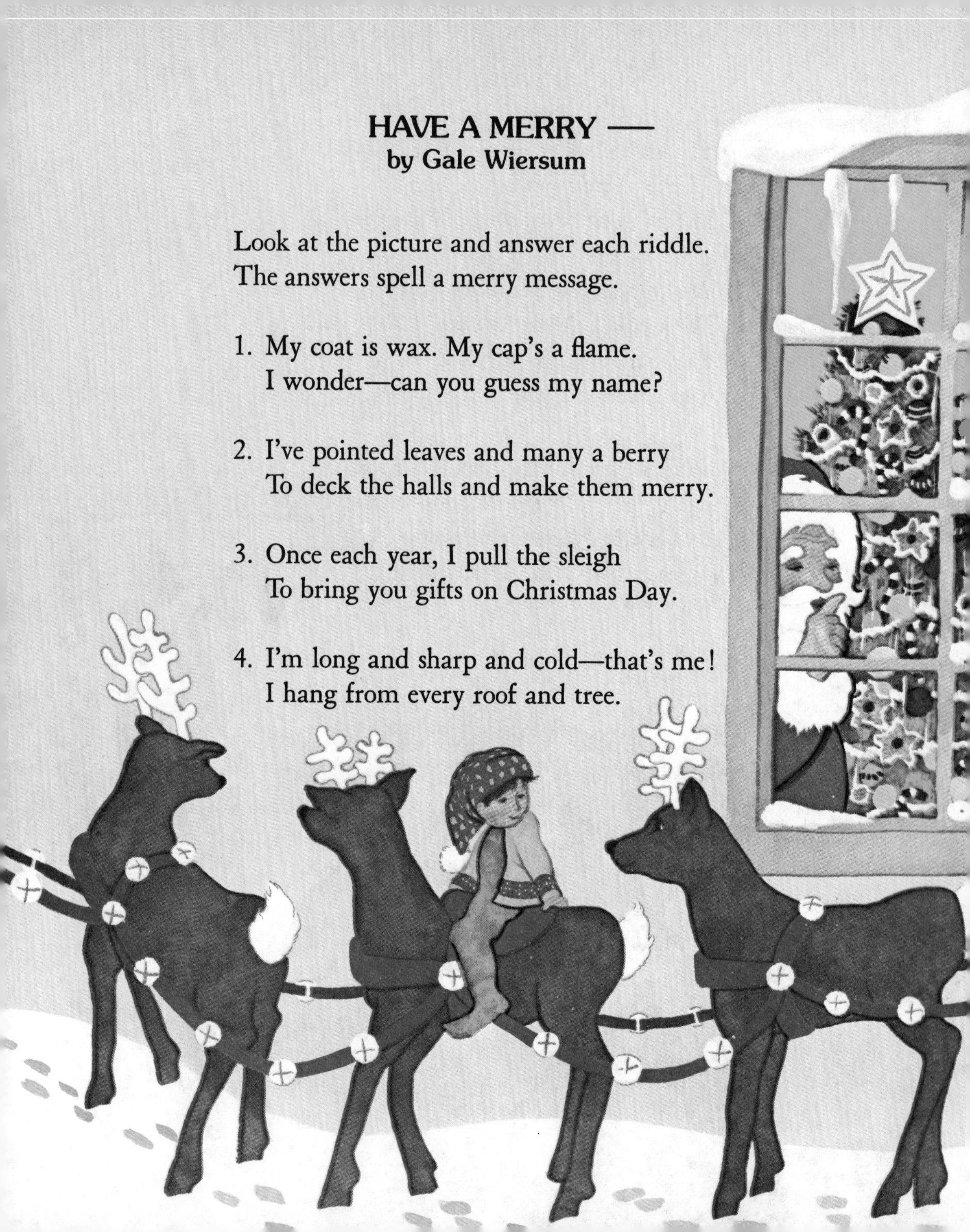

HAVE A MERRY —

by Gale Wiersum

Look at the picture and answer each riddle.
The answers spell a merry message.

1. My coat is wax. My cap's a flame.
   I wonder—can you guess my name?

2. I've pointed leaves and many a berry
   To deck the halls and make them merry.

3. Once each year, I pull the sleigh
   To bring you gifts on Christmas Day.

4. I'm long and sharp and cold—that's me!
   I hang from every roof and tree.

5. I'm placed atop the tree so high,
   I almost reach my home—the sky.

6. I'm draped in tinsel and colorful balls;
   I'm waiting proudly when Santa calls.

7. My berries are white, and my leaves are dark green.
   A kiss you'll receive if beneath me you're seen.

8. My gown is white. The harp I hold
   Is made of cardboard painted gold.

9. I carry lots of games and toys
   For all good little girls and boys.

1 Candle
2 Holly
3 Reindeer
4 Icicle
5 Star
6 Tree
7 Mistletoe
8 Angel
9 Sleigh

THE LIGHTS ON THE CHRISTMAS TREE

by Florence Page Jaques

Once the Christmas tree lights were not lights at all. They were the colors in the rainbow—just an everyday rainbow—the good kind you see in the sky after a rain! When Santa Claus made the very first Christmas tree, it was easy to see that he needed a rainbow for a decoration, because he had only white decorations.

He lived at the North Pole then, you know, as he does now, and when he had powdered the tree with snow and hung icicles all over it and tied snowballs on the ends of the branches, he looked at it and said, "No. It's pretty, but it ought to have some color on it. It needs some red and green and blue and gold—"

"Oh, Santa Claus," said the Littlest White Bear, "let's put a rainbow on it!"

"That's just what it needs," Santa Claus agreed. "I'll send the Biggest White Bear to get one."

"Oh!" said the Littlest White Bear. He was so disappointed that tears came to his eyes. "I was the one who thought of the rainbow. I thought you might let me find it!"

"All right, then," Santa Claus said kindly. "But you must be *very* careful. Rainbows are easy to break, you know, so you must take care not to drop it."

"Oh, I will be careful," promised the Littlest Bear, and he ran and ran on his fat little legs till he found the most beautiful rainbow. Then he picked it and hung it over his back and went home to Santa Claus, walking very carefully. He walked safely past the snowfields and safely past the icebergs and safely past the slippery slides, and at last he came to Santa Claus's steps. He saw Santa Claus in the doorway, waiting.

"Hurrah!" The Littlest White Bear laughed, waving his little front paws in triumph. "Here it is! I found the biggest, best, most beautiful rainbow!"

And just then, both his back feet slipped, and—BOOM! He fell on his back, and the rainbow was broken into a thousand pieces.

"Don't cry; don't cry," said Santa Claus, hurrying down the steps. "You aren't hurt!"

"No, but the rainbow is," sobbed the Littlest White Bear, "and I tried so hard to be careful."

"Never you mind." Santa Claus patted him gently. "We'll put the pieces of the rainbow on the tree. After all, the colors are still just as pretty."

So they picked up a blue piece and put it here, and they picked up a red piece and put it there, and the Christmas tree was prettier than if the rainbow had been all together.

"Oh," said the Littlest White Bear, "I'm glad I fell down!"

And ever since then, we have had beautiful rainbow-colored lights on the Christmas tree.

CHRISTMAS EVERYWHERE
by Phillips Brooks

Everywhere, everywhere, Christmas tonight!
Christmas in lands of the fir tree and pine,
Christmas in lands of the palm tree and vine,
Christmas where snow peaks stand solemn and white,
Christmas where cornfields lie sunny and bright!

For the Christ Child who comes is the Master of all;
No palace too great and no cottage too small.